The Water

Written and photographed by
Anjeanetta Prater Matthews

It is so hot in the summer! That's why we go to the water park.

First, my little brother puts on a life jacket.

It will keep him safe.

He gets on the slide first.

Splash! He slides into the water.

Next, we float down the river in our tube.

Now, we have lunch at our

picnic table.

We are so hungry!

At last, it is time to ride our
favorite boat ride.

It is scary but fun!

We scream all the way down!

It is getting dark and the
park is closed.

We are so tired, but we had
a fun day at the water park!